Ganesha goes to a party

by

Nishita Chaitanya

C·H·I·N·M·A·Y·A   B·A·L·A   K·A·T·H·A

There was once a rich man called Kubera.   He liked being rich.   He really liked being very rich.

He lived in a big palace in the clouds.   He wore grand clothes, with lots of jewellery.   He had big cars, a big boat and a big, big airplane.

One day Kubera thought, "I should have a party in my palace. I shall call everyone I know.   I'll even invite Lord Shiva!"

And so he started getting everything ready.   He told the cooks to cook and the cleaners to clean. He wanted everything to be bright and beautiful.

Kubera then flew to the mountains in his noisy big airplane to invite Lord Shiva.   He gave Lord Shiva a big card with beautiful gold writing.

When Lord Shiva saw Kubera and his shiny card, he smiled.   Lord Shiva knew that Kubera was just showing off.

"I won't come to your party," said Lord Shiva.

"Oh, but you must come, you have to come, please do come…," said Kubera.

Lord Shiva smiled again. "I shall not come. But if you like, you may take my little son, Ganesha."

Kubera thought that to have Lord Shiva's son was better than to have no one at all. So Kubera agreed to take Ganesha.

As they were leaving, Lord Shiva said to Kubera, "Remember, this little boy has a very big tummy, and he loves to eat A LOT of food!"

Kubera replied, "Don't worry, my Lord. I have plenty of food. I have plenty of everything!"

KUBERA - 001

So little Ganesha, with his chubby little hands, chubby little tummy, and chubby little feet, walked hand in hand with Kubera towards his big bright airplane.

When they arrived at the palace, Kubera gave Ganesha lots of nice presents, and he showed off his BIG fancy house to the little boy.

Little Ganesha started thinking about all the yummy food and became very, very hungry!

He climbed into the fancy chair at the big table. There was a golden plate for him, a golden spoon, a golden glass, and golden everything.

Wherever he looked, there was food. Food in the golden pots, food in the golden pans and food on the golden plates!

Little Ganesha loved his food!   So he quickly started eating.   But the more he ate, the more he wanted!   And the faster he ate, the faster it was all finished!

The servants ran back and forth into the kitchen bringing out more and more food.   Back and forth, back and forth, back and forth they went…. but it just wasn't enough!

"I'm hungry," cried Ganesha, "I want MORE."

The servants hurried and scurried, and then started getting worried.

More and more, faster and faster the food all disappeared into Ganesha's chubby little tummy!

All the food on the table was finished. So little Ganesha went into the kitchen. Stretching out his chubby little hands he started eating the food right out of the pots.

Very soon all the cooked food in Kubera's palace was over. So little Ganesha started eating all the raw food.

"I'm STILL hungry," said Ganesha. "Give me more!"

Now the servants got very worried. Kubera also got worried. Everyone got worried. There was no more food. What would they do?

But Ganesha was so hungry he started eating the golden pots, pans and plates!   He put anything and everything into his surprisingly small mouth.

Oh, no!   Now he started eating up Kubera's palace!   On and on and on he went – eating and eating and eating......

Nothing seemed to satisfy him.   Ganesha just kept eating.

Kubera didn't know what to do. So he jumped into his noisy big airplane and quickly flew to Lord Shiva's house. Crying, Kubera said, "Oh great Lord, please forgive me. I am sorry for showing off.

"I have so much food, and so many servants, I have so much money, but none of it can make little Ganesha full – he is still hungry."

"What can I do? Save me, please help me, he is eating up my entire house!" Kubera said.

The ever-peaceful Lord Shiva smiled.   He took a handful of puffed rice and gave it to Kubera. "Here, this will make him full," said Lord Shiva.

Kubera rushed back home and Ganesha was STILL eating. He quickly gave Ganesha the puffed rice and…. it was like magic! Ganesha stopped eating.

Little Ganesha patted his chubby little tummy. "Ahh…." He was now very, very happy indeed. He was full – FINALLY!

The bread did not make him full.   The bananas did not make him full.   The vegetables did not make him full.   Even the pots and pans did not make him full!   But the puffed rice finally made him full.

Do you know why?

Because his father, Lord Shiva, sent him the rice with lots of love.

Things make us hungry, but love makes us full.

Do you know who Ganesha will be visiting next?
....It might just be you!

And you know what to feed him, don't you?